Published by Lee's Press and Publishing Company
www.LeesPress.net

A Premiere Self-Publishing Services Company

ISBN: 979-8-9886270-1-2

This book is dedicated to my babies, the real "Lynn and Margie," Mya-Lynn and Morgan, my fraternal twin girls, who has made the best out of being home while going through some challenging transitions. Mama is proud of you and "I love you this much" (with the widest arms possible). Thank you for teaching me how to love unconditionally. I will always be your mommy, aka "your chubby fuzzy cute mama baby!" 🩶🩶🩶

I would also like to dedicate this book to God my Creator, my Mommy, Ms. Lynn Campbell, and sister, Sharon Cruise, who I love dearly and who have supported me through thick and thin. To my very best friends of 20+years Renny Matthews, Tamika Brown "Miller" LMSW, and Keisha Parris who I love and can depend on to carry me through. Thank you "Keish," who has inspired me to consistently pursue my passion of completing this book... Love you all dearly!

Lastly, Special thanks to: My (Therapist) Tricia Holness LCSW-R, MBA, (Therapist) Tiffany Downing LMHC, (Spiritual Advisor) Chaplin Hare Varnon, (Attorney) Sandy Monroe, (Author/Publisher) Sheniqua Johnson, and Mommy Cassilda Knowles. To my incredible work family, my colleagues and wonderful Supervisors at NYC Department of Health & Mental Hygiene (Bureau of Child Care); Love you all my "Party People". To Our Lady of Grace School (Principal) Richard Helmrich and Teaching faculty. Last but not least, Special thanks to William Lee at Lee's Press and Publishing Company aka "The Publishing Superman," and (Illustrator) Cameron Wilson, aka Cam da Illa Strata'...Thank you! Thank you!

Lynn and Margie's Listening Ears

Written by
Jacklyn Campbell, M.S.Ed.

Lynn and Margie are two of a kind. They are **fraternal twin** sisters. This means they were born on the same day, but they look different and have two different personalities.

1.

Lynn has beautiful dark brown skin and wears glasses for reading. Lynn's favorite stuffed animals are Giraffe and Sparkle. Her favorite color is purple. Lynn is reserved, calm, shy, a little sassy, and loves to read, sing, dance, and play with her Barbie dolls.

Margie looks the exact opposite of Lynn. Margie has beautiful caramel skin with full cheeks. Her favorite stuffed animals are Puppy and Fluffy. Her favorite color is pink. Margie is **rambunctious** and energetic. She loves math, telling jokes, can be a little **mischievous**, loves gymnastics, and playing with her Barbie dolls.

3.

Although the girls are very different, they share two things: they are sisters and at times have a hard time LISTENING WITH THEIR EARS.

"Margie, Lynn, where are you? It's time to wash your face, brush your teeth, and eat some breakfast. I made your absolute favorite pancakes, scrambled eggs, sausage, and some hot cocoa. Hurry now because you must eat, then change into your uniforms," Mama says. "Being that we can't go to school, we must do our work from home," Mama reminds them. **Simultaneously**, Lynn and Margie say, "We know, we know, we can't go to school because of the **Coronavirus**!"

5.

"I can't wait until the **Coronavirus** is over. I feel like we don't get to do anything," Lynn says. "Now, Lynn, if you finish your work, you'll be able to do something special today," Mama says.

Lynn decides to walk to the bathroom to listen to her mom and brush her teeth. Margie sneakily steps into the bathroom and says, "Lynn, let's not listen to Mama, let's play with our tablets and build a house for our dolls. Mama is on the computer and is too busy to even notice. Lynn agrees and says, "Okay, sounds like a plan."

7.

Suddenly, Mama walks into the bedroom and **exclaims**, "Excuse me, girls, I don't see you changing into your uniforms. Please clean up this mess at once, get up, and change so you're not late for class. I do not want to speak to you again!"

8.

Lynn begins to whine and states, "It's all Margie's fault. I don't want to go to class; it's going to take tooooooooooo long." "Well, I'm tired, I'm hungry, and I want to play. I don't want to do my schoolwork," Margie says.

9.

Using her **imagination**, Margie says, "I wish I could go outside and go on an **adventure**. I would go to gymnastics class and do 1,000 flips, I would swing on the monkey bars at Kids Playhouse, and I would jump out of an airplane and land on my two feet."

Lynn also began to use her **imagination** and says, "I would go back to ballet, visit some doll stores, sing on a huge stage, and have a princess party with my friends from school again."

With a **disgruntled** face, Margie and Lynn say, "We can't do those things because of **Coronavirus**... we don't want to do our schoolwork... we just want to play..." In tears, Lynn and Margie **exclaimed!** The girls begin to have a **tantrum** and even start to kick, scream, and throw their toys.

Angry

Happy

Love

Sad

13.

Mama stated, "Alright, that's it with you two. Let's calm down, put our listening ears on, and have a little chat in our special area. Now let's breathe, 1, 2, 3, breathe in, breathe out."

"Now listen, the two of you. I understand this is a very hard time for you, as it is for many other children who are home. It is a hard time for me as well. Mama must work at home on the computer, and you must do schoolwork from the computer as well. Many of the fun places are closed right now. Things are not like they used to. I tell you what, maybe we can wear our masks this afternoon and ride our bicycles throughout the neighborhood," Mama says.

"This is only if you LISTEN with your ears and do your schoolwork. And LISTEN, if we are sad or angry, we never ever shout, scream, or throw toys. We just use our words. Listening is a big part of being a big kid! How do you think Mama feels when you don't listen?" Both girls turn to each other and say, "A little sad?" "A little sad? Not even," Mama replies.

"When you don't listen to Mama, as much as I will always love both of you, I feel like my head is going to pop, I feel hot, my heart hurts, my ears ring, my eyes burn, and my throat gets sore. I feel very, very, very angry, but I don't have a tantrum," Mama said.

"On the other hand, when you do listen, I feel calm, relaxed, and sweet. I listen to you when you ask for your favorite breakfast, pancakes, scrambled eggs, sausage, and hot cocoa. It would make me feel so much better if you could listen more," Mama continues.

18.

Simultaneously, both girls say, "Okay, Mama, we're sorry. We will listen." "Now, let's clean up the mess, come together, and make some home rules to help us to listen better. Can we think of anything?" Mama says.
19.

The girls began to say...

1. "We will use our words when we're sad or angry."
2. "We will do our schoolwork."
3. "We will use our walking feet at home."
4. "We will use kind words to each other."
5. "We will speak with inside voices."
6. "We will clean up our toys in our room."
7. "We will go to bed on time."
8. "We will listen to Mama."

"I am so very proud of you two. I love you, Lynn and Margie. Thank you for listening," Mama says.

21.

28

Vocabulary Words

1) **Adventure-** an exciting experience or activity.

2) **Coronavirus-** a very bad cold that can cause harmful sickness.

3) **Disgruntled-** to be unhappy.

4) **Exclaim-** to cry out in surprise, pain, or, anger.

5) **Fraternal Twins-** two siblings who are born the same day but look different.

6) **Imagination-** To think of new ideas with images in your mind.

7) **Mischievous-** disobedient or misbehaving.

8) **Rambunctious-** active and noisy.

9) **Simultaneously-** at the same time.

10) **Tantrum-** to have an outburst or blow up.

Parent Resources/Tips

1. (Reference page 13) "Special Area;" is a cozy corner. This area should never be used as a form of punishment but rather a place to think and express feelings. To create a cozy corner, use soft materials. You can include a small couch, books, pictures of feelings, anda canopy.

2. (Reference pages 15,17) Attempting to remain calm when children throw tantrums can be challenging. Speak to them at eye level and use breathing techniques to calm them down. The overall goal is to validate their emotions and to encourage self-regulated behaviors.

3. (Reference pages 15-17) When the adult expresses his/her feelings, children will listen effectively as their desire is not to hurt your feelings. Even when you are angry, after you take deep breaths, ensure that you express how much you love them.

4. (Reference pages 19-20) Creating rules together is essential. Young children desire to be part of decision making. If they can write let them write and create rules.

5. (Reference by: Bank Street) Center for Emotionally Responsive Practice at Bank Street.

6. Say what you mean and mean what you say! Set clear expectations, explain you will do something, and praise children once they listen to your words. Ensure you reward them if they do (this could be with encouraging words of praise, a high five, or even a sticker).

7. The importance of praise: it can build a child's self-esteem, self-worth, and fosters autonomy.

8. Activities that can be done at home during/after the coronavirus pandemic: painting, making a volcano, making playdough from scratch, bookmaking, talent shows, baking, board games, and neighborhood walks

9. As parents, we have noticed effects our children have faced due to the pandemic including social, emotional, as well as academical effects. There has been a significant decline in grades. Please ensure you are having healthy ongoing transparent conversations with your child's teacher regarding strengthening their academics. In addition, maintaining an open mind to consent for additional support in place if needed. The overall goal is to reinforce 100% success.

Continue to Protect yourself from the Coronavirus by wearing a mask, consistently washing hands, and maintaining 6 feet social distancing!

My name is Jacklyn Campbell, and I was born and raised in the Bronx, New York, of a Jamaican descent background. I have been in the Early Childhood Education field for over 18 years. I have worked in various capacities as a Children's Ministry Leader and Children's choir leader at church, Counselor, Teacher, Director of Childcare programs, Education Director, and currently serving as a Senior Early Childhood Education Consultant Supervisor for The New York City Department of Health. I have obtained a Master's degree in Early Childhood Education, and my passion has always been to encourage children's overall social/emotional, cognitive, language, and physical development. My experience with children over the years has led me to this crucial point of where we are in the world today. In 2020, During this horrific pandemic, I have gone through a major transition in my marital status, which has influenced me to utilize the skills I have acquired as an educator and single parent of now 9-year-old fraternal twin girls. This challenging transition has given me the driving force to fulfill my long-time passion for writing a children's book. I wanted to share my experience while working remotely and supporting my young children during remote learning. One of my favorite educational quotes is by Early Childhood Specialist Lisa Murphy, "If this was your child's last day on earth, what would they remember?"

My prayer is that this book will inspire and support single parents as they continue to help children cope effectively who are home during this pandemic and dealing with the current effects of COVID-19. Although this pandemic has been challenging for many adults, it is imperative that we understand children's emotions during this time and create positive and memorable experiences for them that will last a lifetime!
In my spare time, I enjoy attending services, writing, listening to music, shopping, comedy shows, spas, knitting, helping those in need, and spending time with my family and close friends.

Please read and enjoy! 😊

Milton Keynes UK
Ingram Content Group UK Ltd.
UKHW051835040823
426344UK00003B/35